Raintree is an imprint of Capstone Global Library Limited, a company incorporated in England and Wales having its registered office at 7 Pilgrim Street, London, EC4V 6LB - Registered company number: 6695582

To contact Raintree please phone 0845 6044371, fax + 44 (0) 1865 312263, or email myorders@ raintreepublishers.co.uk. Customers from outside the UK please telephone +44 1865 312262.

Originally published by DC Comics in the U.S. in single magazine form as Superman Adventures #5. Copyright © 2013 DC Comics. All Rights Reserved.

DC Comics
1700 Broadway, New York, NY 10019, USA
A Warner Bros. Entertainment Company

First published by Stone Arch Books in 2013
First published in the United Kingdom in 2014
The moral rights of the proprietor have been asserted.

Ashley C. Andersen Zantop *Publisher*
Michael Dahl *Editorial Director*
Donald Lemke & Sean Tulien *Editors*
Heather Kindseth *Creative Director*
Bob Lentz *Designer*
Kathy McColley *Production Specialist*

**DC COMICS**
Mike McAvennie *Original US Editor*
Rick Burchett & Terry Austin *Cover Artists*

Originated by Capstone Global Library Ltd
Printed and bound in China by Leo Paper Products Ltd

ISBN 978 1 406 26679 5
17 16 15 14 13
10 9 8 7 6 5 4 3 2

*British Library Cataloguing in Publication Data*
A full catalogue record for this book is available from the British Library.

# SUPERMAN ADVENTURES

## Balance of Power

Scott McCloud..................... writer
Bret Blevins.....................penciller
Terry Austin ......................... inker
Marie Severin.................. colourist
Lois Buhalis...................... letterer

Superman created by
Jerry Siegel & Joe Shuster

8

13

NO NEED TO WASTE YOUR BREATH. I AGREE, SHE'S COSTING MY ENTERTAINMENT DIVISIONS A LOT OF MONEY. I SUPPOSE SHE HAS TO BE ELIMINATED SOMEHOW.

AH, WELL, HOW CAN I BE OF SERVICE?

YOUR WEAPONS DIVISION HAS BEEN WORKING ON SOME *ELECTROMAGNETIC PULSE GENERATORS.*

PITY. IT WAS ALMOST WORTH IT, SEEING YOU HUMILIATED.

YES, WE HAVE SEVERAL PROTOTYPES. THEY CAN DISRUPT ELECTRICAL FIELDS--

--BUT THEY'RE MOSTLY GOOD FOR *SHORT RANGE* USE.

THAT'S ALL I NEED. I'M GOING TO LURE HER INTO A CONFRONTATION. ALL I NEED FROM *YOU* IS THAT YOU CUT OFF HER *ESCAPE* ROUTE.

I WANT HER *SURROUNDED* AND *CONTAINED.* LEAVE THE REST TO ME.

I KNOW YOU'RE OUT THERE, GUYS, SAYING, "WHAT ARE WE GONNA DO ABOUT THIS CRAZY CHICK? HOW ARE WE GONNA PUT HER DOWN?"

WELL, I GOT *NEWS* FOR YOU, BOYS. THIS "CRAZY CHICK" IS HERE TO STAY!

WELL, YOU'VE GOT TO ADMIT SHE HAS A LOT OF *STYLE*...FOR A *PSYCHOPATH*, I MEAN.

GIVE ME A BREAK, ANGELA! IT'S *CENSORSHIP*, PURE AND SIMPLE!

SO GET USED TO THE NEW WORLD ORDER. WE NOW RETURN TO OUR REGULARLY SCHEDULED 100% FEMALE PROGRAMMING!

MAYBE. BUT THE FALLOUT HASN'T BEEN *ALL* BAD.

I MEAN, *DON'T GET ME WRONG*, SHE HAS TO BE *STOPPED* AND ALL, BUT IT'S BEEN FUN DOING THE *REAL* NEWS-CASTS.

I LIKE THE CHANCE TO PLAY *SERIOUS JOURNALIST* FOR A CHANGE. AND YOU *KNOW* I'M *BET'ER* AT IT THAN THAT EMPTY-SUIT ANCHORMAN, *REGGIE BANKS*.

WELL, YOU OUGHT TO APPLY FOR THAT JOB THEN, BUT DON'T TAKE *HANDOUTS* FROM *TERRORISTS*.

I TAKE WHAT I CAN GET, *LOIS!*

THAT'S WHAT BEING IN JOURNALISM IS ALL ABOUT. IT'S ABOUT TAKING YOUR OPPORTUNITIES WHEN YOU GET THEM. IT'S ABOUT LOOKING OUT FOR *NUMBER ONE*.

*Oh, REALLY?* I THOUGHT IT WAS ABOUT THE *TRUTH*.

YEAH, THAT, TOO.

THE BATTLE HAS BEEN RAGING FOR SEVERAL MINUTES--

--BUT NEITHER OPPONENT SEEMS TO HAVE THE UPPER HAND!

IN THE LAST MINUTE OR SO, THOUGH, WE'VE SEEN SEVERAL MEN MOVING IN TOWARD THE FRONT ROWS WITH SOME MACHINERY WE CAN'T IDENTIFY, AND NEARBY...

...YES, I BELIEVE I SEE LEX LUTHOR!

READY, MEN! ACTIVATE NOW!

WHO ARE THEY? YOUR CAVALRY?

THEY'RE NOT HERE TO FIGHT YOU, LIVE-WIRE. THEY'RE HERE TO CONTAIN YOU!

WE'VE GOT YOU SURROUNDED! ≥Unnh!≤ NO MATTER WHAT...THE OUTCOME OF OUR BATTLE, YOU'RE FINISHED! YOU CAN'T... ESCAPE THIS ROOM!

WHAT?!

Sha-KOW!!

...AND AS THE PARA-MEDICS ARRIVE, IT LOOKS LIKE WE CAN CLOSE THIS CHAPTER.

THIS HAS BEEN A SPECIAL REPORT BROUGHT TO YOU BY YOUR... SPECIAL REPORTER, ANGELA CHEN. WE'LL BE BACK FOR SOME ANALYSIS AFTER THESE WORDS.

*THANKS,* ANGELA. I'LL TAKE IT FROM HERE.

LOOKS LIKE THE AIR WAVES ARE *CLEAR* AGAIN.

OH. HI, REGGIE. ARE YOU SURE YOU DON'T WANT ME TO, *UH...* FINISH UP THE REPORT?

NO, THAT'LL BE ALL NOW. CAN I--

--HAVE THE MICROPHONE NOW?

THANKS, BABE.

*...LIVE IN* TEN SECONDS...

HEY, LOIS, WANT TO CATCH SOME DINNER? I COULD USE SOME *FRESH AIR*.

SURE.

## SCOTT McCLOUD *WRITER*

Scott McCloud is an acclaimed comics creator and author whose best-known work is the graphic novel *Understanding Comics*. His work also includes the science-fiction adventure series *Zot!*, a 12-issue run of *Superman Adventures*, and much more. Scott is the creator of the "24 Hour Comic", and frequently lectures on comics theory.

## BRET BLEVINS *PENCILLER*

Bret Blevins is a professional comic book and animation artist. He has worked with today's top publishers and animation studios, including DC Comics, Marvel, Dark Horse, Disney, and Warner Bros. He has illustrated some of the world's best-known characters, like Batman, Superman, the Incredible Hulk, and more!

## TERRY AUSTIN *INKER*

Throughout his career, inker Terry Austin has received dozens of awards for his work on high-profile comics for DC Comics and Marvel, such as *The Uncanny X-Men*, *Doctor Strange*, *Justice League America*, *Green Lantern*, and *Superman Adventures*. He lives in New York, USA.

admirer  one who likes or respects another

censored  banned from sight or use

disgust  cause a strong feeling against something

dominated  controlled or ruled

fallout  the result of an action

feminist  someone who believes strongly that women should have equal rights and opportunities that men have

instantaneous  occuring, done, or completed in an instant

lure  attract someone or some creature into a trap

machinery  group of machines, or parts of a machine

prototype  original model on which something is based

ransom  money that is demanded for the release of someone who is being held captive

surrender  give up, or admit that you are beaten in a fight or battle

# SUPERMAN GLOSSARY

**Clark Kent:** Superman's alter ego, Clark Kent, is a reporter for the *Daily Planet* newspaper and was raised by Jonathan and Martha Kent. No one knows he is Superman except for his adopted parents, the Kents.

**The Daily Planet:** the city of Metropolis's biggest and most read newspaper. Clark, Lois, Jimmy, and Perry all work for the *Daily Planet.*

**Lex Luthor:** Lex believes Superman is a threat to Earth and must be stopped. He will do anything it takes to bring the Man of Steel to his knees.

**Livewire:** Livewire can absorb and release electrical energy up to extremely high voltages. She can also transform into living energy and seemingly teleport across power lines and other sources of electricity.

**Lois Lane:** like Clark Kent, Lois is a reporter at the *Daily Planet.* She is also one of Clark's best friends.

**Mercy Graves:** Mercy is Lex Luthor's personal assistant and bodyguard. She is fiercely loyal to Lex and is never far from his side.

**Metropolis:** the city where Clark Kent (Superman) lives.

**S.T.A.R. Labs:** a research centre in Metropolis, where scientists make high-tech tools and devices for Superman and other heroes.

# VISUAL QUESTIONS & PROMPTS

**1** In this panel, Livewire uses the word "power" in two ways at once. What are the two ways that "power" can be interpreted in this panel? Explain your answer.

**2** In this panel, Livewire is reacting to what is being said in the speech bubbles. How do you think she feels in this panel? Why?

**3** Why do you think Mercy Graves turned back to look at Livewire and Superman? What do you think she was feeling and thinking? Explain your answers.

**4** In this panel, we see an outline of Livewire. Using details, describe what you think has just happened in this panel.

**5** Livewire's hands are blurred in this panel. Why do you think the creators of this comic decided to show her this way?

**6** At the end of this comic book, this is Superman's expression. How do you think he feels about the outcome of the events? Why?

# SUPERMAN ADVENTURES